C000260356

Henrietta Rogers.

Specimen Sight-Reading Tests for Cello

Grades 1-5

The Associated Board of
the Royal Schools of Music

GRADE 1

AB 2661

GRADE 1

GRADE 1

Risoluto

17

Alla valse

18

Moderato

19

AB 2661

GRADE 2

GRADE 2

GRADE 3

GRADE 3

AB 2661

GRADE 4

GRADE 4

GRADE 5

GRADE 5

GRADE 5

AB 2661

Printed in England by Caligraving Limited, Thetford, Norfolk

2:03